Esther Dreher
Ethan Lowe
Oz Hardwick

Portmanteau

Indigo Dreams Publishing

First Edition: Portmanteau
First published in Great Britain in 2017 by:
Indigo Dreams Publishing
24, Forest Houses
Cookworthy Moor
Halwill
Beaworthy
Devon
EX21 5UU

www.indigodreams.co.uk

The authors have asserted their rights under the Copyright, Designs and Patents Act 1988 to be identified as the authors of this work.
© 2017

ISBN 978-1-910834-63-3

British Library Cataloguing in Publication Data. A CIP record for this book can be obtained from the British Library.

Designed and typeset in Palatino Linotype by Indigo Dreams.
Cover design by Michael Knapp.
Printed and bound in Great Britain by 4Edge Ltd.
www.4edge.co.uk

Papers used by Indigo Dreams are recyclable products made from wood grown in sustainable forests following the guidance of the Forest Stewardship Council.

For writers who consider themselves to be:
hybridactive, schizofrenetic, complexicated, contradexterous,
and fantabulous.

CONTENTS

Part Two

Foreword

"Portmanteau, what does *that* mean?"
This was a question wafting through the air of Leeds Trinity University during the early stages of our call for submissions to this year's anthology. Creative individuals with a passion for words, yet unfamiliar with this particular noun, were intrigued enough to look it up. To those who threw puzzled looks in our direction, forgive us if we 'condesplained'.

In fact, our own discovery of the word began when we googled *Brexit* in an attempt to find a theme with specific relevance to the year of publication. 2017: a historical time of change, a climate of uncertainty, and the word *Brexit* on the front of every paper almost every day of the year so far. Once we had our attention drawn to these linguistic hybrids, we started noticing portmanteaus everywhere. *Brexit, regrexit, Bre-entry, Cuckservative, Trumpeachment*; read any news report dated 2017 and it doesn't take long to spot one.

But the scope for theme-linking or 'thlinking' was much wider than *Brexit* and politics alone. Unpacking the portmanteau definition— one word made up out of two combined, as coined by Lewis Carroll from the original meaning of the suitcase that splits into two equal compartments — prompted some distinctive and varied pieces of writing. The result is an anthology of imaginative and original work, neatly packed up into two parts: Poetry and Prose, with a smattering of haiku throughout.

"Why haiku?" was another question posed.
Unpack the Portmanteau and you'll find a whole range of related ideas spilling out, as shown in the writing flowing through this book. On each page we can trace the writer's train of thought, discover their place of arrival, and see the contents of their travelling-bag, expressed in a poem or story. For example, the train journey: Portmanteau — two words blended — parallel ideas — visual synonyms — two things joined or connected; the arrival points: chemical compounds, a married

couple, reflections in a mirror, a voodoo doll. On the other side, examples of 'opposing themes' — two things torn apart or juxtaposed — visual antonyms; the arrival points: conflicting emotions, hiding and seeking, a double-life vivisected, a brain lobotomised by love, the end of a relationship, the scars of separation; and it all brings us back to … *Brexit*.

It was our own train ride through the 'opposing themes' that led us to the decision to include haiku. Traditionally haiku juxtaposes two ideas, placing them within the confines of three lines and approximately seventeen syllables. But traditions are sometimes better off left behind and destroyed like an unattended suitcase on a train platform. In the haiku shown here, you'll see some writers flagrantly breaking haiku conventions like a bunch of post-modernist radicals, with others going for a more conservative approach. Like Corbynistas and Mayniacs, you might say.

Some writers use contemporary portmanteau words as their subject matter, such as 'staycation' and 'spork'; others reach a little further back in time, with 'Britpop' and further still, with 'smog'; while others dream up their own amalgamations. Tim Leadbeater's poem describes these blissful moments of word coinages perfectly:

Ideas spill across the sheets
*   as new words, wet from their coupulation, are conceived.*
Whilst we might cheer on the 'brute' of Andrea Harker's story, as he throws the words *Austerity*, *Weaponise* and *Brexit* into the river to drown, we would have to agree with the story's protagonist when she argues:

"… but… surely it's not the words themselves that cause the problems? It's the people using them."

Which brings us to our final stop on the editing journey, where we open our 'leathery hearts' and express gratitude to all the lovely contributors who have used words to do something positive: to create delightful pieces of poetry and fiction. To you we say 'Moobs!' simply because we like the word.

Esther Dreher and Ethan Lowe

Portmanteau

You see it's like a portmanteau
—there are two meanings packed
up into one word.

— *Alice Through the Looking Glass*
Lewis Carroll

sometimes I can dream

sit inside a star waiting

for life to explode

Part One

small surprise, this form

fuses haikai and hokku –

verballetic poems

Threxit

Pavement cracks widen
    miasma of words rises
        catches in the throat

Fundamenticles

We cannot measure how
subatomic particles communicate:
photons bounce off this paper
at the speed of light
directly into your eye;
but electrons, when hit by photons,
are not what they were.
Where are they?

Is the universe
empty space
filled with particles of matter?
Or a continuum,
an unbroken whole,
alive with intelligence
out of which consciousness separates?
These thoughts grow – but
is thought creating divisions out of itself?*
God does not play dice says Einstein.
Yet Heisenberg keeps cooking,
everything is uncertain.

* *Theory of David Bohm*

Clare Wigzell

Clare Wigzell is writing her way into hope in times of darkness.

Staycation

Select a level site, away from flowing water
to avoid contamination. Steel plates, 3/16 inch thick,
are preferred. The trench you dig must allow
for three feet of earth on top of the roof. Doors, weighing 2800
pounds, are specially designed
to flex and return to form during a blast.
See appendix for how to ventilate your shelter.

The beach was a let-down; the advert
had shown golden sand, a flotilla of sunshades
fluttering in a gentle breeze, under cloudless skies.
This sand is more like grey grit,
and you can't see the sun at all.
There's nothing to eat or drink in the poolside bar.
In fact, there *is* no poolside bar.

Provisions should include bottled water,
canned goods and opener, toilet paper,
hospital grade first aid kit. Potassium iodide tablets.
Stock plenty of plastic sheeting
to seal off areas and shroud bodies.
This may be an extended staycation – up to 28 days, even.
It's always a shock, getting back into the real world
after a break, isn't it? You have to be prepared for that.

Hannah Stone

Hannah Stone reconstructs poems from the broken walls of language.
Less pretentiously, she likes to write.

Smog

Between framed sunlit peaks,
clusters of stars and ethereal lakes,
Teesside was awarded:
    Best industrial landscape.
I could tell that smog anywhere,
forgive pollution for jobs and trade,
honesty and pride stretched years,
spectrum of greys pump above.

Always that burnt earth, meat smell
that I still connect to the horses by the beach
and their factory backdrop.
Salt air left us giddy, free.
Once, with heavy rain,
we sheltered under marram grass
    watching a rainbow straddle the harbour.

    We played in winter snow,
      rolling down
        white caked dunes
          sumo-wrestling in puffa coats.
    The wind stole our breath when we laughed.

Some footprints go deeper than sand
in this landscape full of smog,
a landscape full
of love.

Caroline Wilkinson

*Caroline Wilkinson is fascinated with words and loves to mould them
to her meaning.*

Hide & Seek

If you narrow your eyes
through the warp
      in my glass door
two of everything come into view.
      Any movement
      fragile as breathing
can alter which image appears
          or disappears.
At its dead centre
while doubling purples   yellows and pinks
of last year's impatiens and marigolds peeking
between the cracks
      in my cement steps
            I find myself staring
          at you
walking near   Cope's bushes
    and secret apple trees
      perfect for hide & seek.
    While I am running
to embrace you   sputtering
like a child
  to grasp your hand,
      you   vanish.

Now I stand at my door
nose pressed
eyes centred
squinting
through the pane
    lip syncing
the plea:
Olly Olly Oxen   free!

Honey Pot

Honey's all he gets
stuffing his face in her pot
       her wings fluttering

Sweet Revenge

If I were a bee
I'd sting you in the gonads
       when you come honey

Kathleen Strafford

Kathleen Strafford cruises in a black unmarked car and machine guns adverbs and adjectives. "Good Riddance," she says with righteous indignation (obviously)!

Metaficiality in Arcadia

Actaeon saw the bootilicious
goddess bathing; she spun versions,
split and wrote him – as a man
her artemischief soon melidified

into a dianarchic deerie stag.
In that woodland miraclearing,
as he felt his words dissolve,
writhing in his mantlered stagony,

he saw her watching as his hounds
with such betrayalacrity, such
desirate animalice,
tore apart their master-prey.

Amina Ayal

Amina Alyal enjoys exploring the subtle shades of meaning in the language of poetry.

Coin after Geopoliticus Child

The compressed sphere flatly lies. Its face
to the ground; a plush tale pushing
through hard green;
the edge scuffed and bright,

a halo against tarmac, stained
by incontinent feet that prompt a tang
of panic to bleed from it like a cut tongue.
The ground is dappled red and the metal

belly begins to split; a dilating aperture
weeps while an arm strains
into grey air. A mouth begs
in muted glossolalia, still buried

under the heaving torso's slick
gleaming skin, flexing ribs through
the opening that openly sighs its openness:
the copper flakes away. The curled body breathes.

Someone drops a two-pence piece:
it sings.
     Ich dien.
          Ich dien.
               Ich dien.
                    And rolls away.

John Darley

John Darley likes words: he gathers them together when he writes, and scatters them when he reads.

Yesterfear

It vanished
        as snow on a mountain
becomes a river
        in spring

as a cell divides
        inside a prism of light
 held in

        a clenched fist

she opened
        her hand and with wings
it flew
        to land
in a different place
            fear away

Kathryn Wharton

Kathryn Wharton graduated from the Open University with a Creative Writing degree. Her poetry features in the June 2017 edition of Mslexia.

Jellycopter

There's a jellycopter in my living room.
Knife-sharp rotors beat the air like a whisk,
the frenzy of it thundering
above its flesh-soft sweet underbelly
that wobbles on a wide silver plate.

I'm pinned to the wall by the din of it,
the cat is fucking terrified,
we're both falling to bits.

I wish I'd never got it out of its box,
sent it straight back
to the lunatic I bought it off on Ebay.
There weren't even any instructions and what does that knob
do anyway and
my GOD I think it's going to take off,
rip the house out by its roots,
toss us screaming into the sea.

Paul Vaughan

Paul Vaughan is a Yorkshire poet, hates custard and loves his cat. His poems have been quite widely published, despite everything.

Uninvited

They arrive with bags, cases full of stories, conversation.
I drag them feet first up to their room.

In equal measures they compete
anecdotes   half each. I listen
eyes on parted lips ears on a daydream.

Every morning more.
Cases. Bags.
Split open. Weak coffee
sour milk. Sipped, spilt
mouth, lap floor.

I respond in kind hide foul face
smile then withdraw.

Evenings insist that I join them
sharing leftovers months old, with water.
Imagining beer sausage, chips
I squeeze on obligatory laughter.

Half wishing they were gone. Half loving the tones
of voices, human filling my home.

I cannot live with people. I cannot live alone.

Slactivist Twant

Outie denies intolerance:
I'm not a racist
some of my Facebook friends
are foreigners.

Mindlessness

downing my days
cheap shots knocked back
       – still not drunk

Esther Dreher

Esther Dreher finds that being a Creative Writing student is the
perfect excuse to bury herself in books.

Port-Man-Teau

This will take some explaining, thinks Bob on his way
to buy his Mail. *A general election? Shit!*
It was hard enough telling her how to vote on Brexit.

His gaze follows his neighbour as she walks
her ginormous labradoodle round the corner.
Bootylicious, Bobby slurps. *Extremely magnifique.*

He likes a bit of Franglais, follows the French election,
hopes on the quiet Le Penn will get in. *A woman. Still,*
so is Mrs May, and he's not that keen on the bromances

of your male politicians: *Too pally, you just never know.*
Although he prides himself on his gaydar,
the I.T. guy who fixed his malware soon got told.

At the corner shop he buys his paper, winks. Thinks
This'll shut the Corbynistas up. On his walk back
he recalls the cop who stopped and breathalysed him

on the way home from The Lodge last week: *Dodged*
that one nicely. He glances at the front page, tuts,
flicks through his copy of NUTS, hidden inside.

Gill Lambert

Gill is a poet and a teacher. Both of which have changed her life.

Portmanteau Man

He is a Frenchman
with a portmanteau life,
a girl in each port
and a port in each wife.

A bag in each station,
with passport and clothes:
á double fond,
wherever he goes.

Portant un manteau
fluide et gris,
he comes into Brest, and
goes out like the sea.

Tawny his cloak
in sunny Marseilles,
like the sweet wine of Douro,
le vin Portugais.

A life vivisected,
valise in two parts,
neatly encased in
two leathery hearts.

Rosemary Mitchell

Rosemary Mitchell is a historian and is fascinated by words, and the ways of other human beings.

Lobotomance

Attention idiots: It's a scam.
Love has been marketed to you
by generations of horny morons,
peddling impossible expectations
to get published, get rich, or get laid,
selling dreams of kisses in the rain
and sun-set sex on the beach.
Newsflash, suckers –
Sex on the beach results in a sandy arse crack.

You see, scientifically speaking,
love is a chemical reaction in the brain,
an electric parasite in our neurological circuitry
that compels us to breed.
Emotionally speaking,
love is a sexually transmitted disease
that compels us to cry on busses
and listen to The Smiths
while we stalk our crush on Facebook,
or move to new cities
where we'll 'find ourselves'
sadder, skinter, and more alone than before.

It will happen to you someday, son.
You'll swap a portion of your brain
for a portion of a loving heart
and, my God, it will feel amazing.
The smart people and the cynics
will call you a fool
in aggressively pessimistic poetry,
while you smile, hold her close,
and think to yourself, with what little is left
of your love drunk mind:
Ignorance is bliss.

Masturdating

That's right,
    I go to the cinema alone.

    What's wrong with that?

It's hardly an activity
    enhanced by company,

            is it?

Billy Humphreys

Billy Humphreys – writer, musician, free spirit, idiot.

Port Manteau

Desultry harbour, small steamer in from the east
shrugs off a traveller or two. At the border,
control as she presents carefully creased
documents and the correct word order.
From the café terrace she scans people and news:
Suspected Neologist arrested by agents
of the Archaeologue. Parts of speech used
in word-making found. Call for severe sentence.
A shadow falls upon the page. Taking the back streets,
he hustles her up stairs to a room. They are both relieved
of clothes and loyalties. Ideas spill across the sheets
as new words, wet from their coupulation, are conceived.
Only the healthy contamination of maturity
will cleanse this shabby collaboration with purity.

A-Wain

(homage to Peter Kennard's anti-nuclear photomontage – a visual portmanteau)

A weaponised haywain stands in the stream,
taking on coolant for the transportation team,
dispersed deep in Constable country, fused
into his landscape of English oaks, these cruise
missiles rise ready for the order to rain
bucolic apocalypse on the German plain.

Tim Leadbeater

Tim Leadbeater is delighted to be included in the anthology but knows his poems are very Audenary.

Britpop and me

Travelling aboard the National Express,
Dante's 'The Divine Comedy' in hand,
I'm surrounded by common people, girls and boys.

A charmless man approaches, leering,
leans in slightly
and my stomach lurches from
stale cigarettes and alcohol on his breath.
"Something for the weekend, love?"
"Come again?" I ask.
"Sorted for E's and Whizz?"
I fake a smile, nod, place
the placebo in my mouth, wash it down with Oasis.
"Good enough for me," the dodgy creep says
as he winks and moves along.

Some might say I'm fickle, a sheep, a follower.
I'm not. For me, the drugs don't work.
I'm already high on Britpop.
I feel it: the music beats in my chest,
lyrics flood my mind.
It's as much a part of me
as I am.

I stare out of the window: urban and suburban
pass by in a blur.
Contemplating the end of a century,
I sigh, knowing that Britpop and me-
we're just gonna have to roll with it.

Tracey Myers

Tracey Myers is studying English and Writing at Leeds Trinity.

Plagiarpoem

after Don Paterson

One morning, Don Miguel got out of bed
with one idea planted in his head:
to make one word where once there had been two.
It took our man a day to work it through,
the words they'd joined together at the hip –
jeggings, bromance, mocktail, gaydar, Brexit –
his two words lay there and they wouldn't join:
they should be seamless, two sides of one coin.
Mixed up, the sounds got stuck inside his throat –
bitcoin, Britpop, sharknado, docusoap –
his dark obsession nearly drove him wild:
manbag, mansplaining, manboobs, manchild,

until one day he hit upon the truth –
cowboy and builder? Extension and roof? –
language doesn't alter just like that
(electrocute, Clintonomics, carjack):
there has to be a reason or a need
to take two nouns and get them both to breed.
That's why his pairs lay still, refused to move:
the sense must change, and sense can't be improved.
He split them up, they'd always be apart –
two lonely lovers, chuggers, broken hearts.
Except they're words, and words don't ache or pout.
And words are all this poem is about.

Ian Harker

Ian Harker's first collection, Rules of Survival, *is forthcoming from Templar Poetry in the autumn.*

Refractive Index

Glass swallows sand, swallows roses:
glass swallows fire. The year is out of
balance, stumbling like a drunk between
ice and sun, numb fingered and shaking.

Glass swallows tungsten, swallows mercury:
glass swallows water. There are unexplained
shapes in the night sky, flipping between
the Moon and Venus, dodging spectral analysis.

Glass swallows distance, swallows hands:
glass swallows air. If a train leaves a station
at 9.30, travelling west, averaging 57 mph,
is there any guarantee that we'll meet again?

Glass swallows lips, swallows eyes:
glass swallows earth. In an empty church,
windows crack like webs and bones scrape
lost music. I swallow the glass, feel it

thumbing my throat, my chest; feel it
concatenating to sand, its sorites paradox
vitrifying at the base of my sternum,
molding me into reflections of myself.

brief poems flicker
on A64 verges
– lonely hitch-haiku

Frankly, says Rhett Butler,
stroking his pencil moustache,
I don't give a damn
    about lines and syllables.

seasons and objects
offer myself in haiku
– all you see is frogs

Oz Hardwick

Oz Hardwick lives somewhere between York, Plymouth, Bruges and Tanelorn. He is currently Professor of English at Leeds Trinity University.

beside the still creek

fleshy corpse turned inside out

greets the vulture's beak

Part Two

a bossy voice blows

Wake up and smell the coffee

as you dream of tea

I stare, pen in hand

at the blank page. It has no

interest in me.

One Night in Port Manteau

Smog cloaked the back streets near the harbour, so dense that Anna, standing with her sister beneath their lamppost, couldn't make out even the closest of the other pairs. She felt Maria shudder; from the cold, no doubt, but it was as if the enveloping murk itself had spooked her.

"We'll be inside soon," Anna said, in their language, breath smoky in the night air.

"You reckon the boat will dock in this?"

"The boat always docks."

It was true. Since the government had conferred special status on the port – and the sisters and their kind had been relocated – the tourist boats came without fail.

"Snuggle up to me, if you're cold," Anna said, deadpan.

The trick materialised like an apparition, sheathed in white waterproofs that resembled a hazmat suit. Fiftysomething. Overweight. Nervous. The usual, Anna thought.

"Hey there, ladies," he said, managing a smile. American. Or Canadian.

"Hey," Maria replied, in English. "How you doing?"

Anna said nothing. Her sister played the friendly half of the double act.

His chubby face damp with mizzle, he looked from one to the other. Desire clung to the guy like an aura. Anna detected something else, though. Sadness. Or fear. Just then, a moped raced by and he flinched like someone had shot at him.

"What're your names?" he asked. Whispered, almost.

"Anna," Anna replied, a microsecond before her sister added, "Maria."

Anna-Maria.

By the time they'd walked round the corner to the motel, they knew more about him than Anna cared to. Larry. Fifty-six. Lived in Monterey. Worked in telemarketing for FedEx. *I'm a workaholic.* One brother. Dead. No mention of a wife or kids.

When he asked where they were originally from, they said Tanzania. That week's answer.

If it made this seem like a date to him, that was fine by Anna. In an hour they would already have started to forget him.

At the check-in desk, Bastian was watching an OJ Simpson biopic on Netflix. "First visit to Port Manteau, sir?" he asked, setting the iPad aside. The trick – Larry – said it was. Bastian took him through the house rules; took his payment.

In the room, the sisters went over to the window and Anna lowered the blind, shutting out the light from the Cineplex opposite. Larry had already slipped off the waterproofs, to reveal brown cords and a mustard V-neck stretched taut over impressive moobs.

They stripped for him. Let him take a long look at them, naked. His face had turned so pale Anna wondered if he was about to faint. When they started to undress him, he stopped them. "Can we switch that off first?" he asked, gesturing at the bedside lamp. Shy type.

"Sure," Maria said.

He chose to start with Maria – they often did; although the sisters were identical, Maria's friendliness made her seem the prettier. Typically, the trick would have a good feel of Anna while he was fucking Maria. Not Larry. Difficult as it was, he contrived not to touch her at all. Again, fine by her. She stared up at black expanse of ceiling, riding each jolt of the mattress, the tug-tug-tug of her sister. Closing her mind to the cheeseburger stink of Larry's sweat. Drifting. Waiting her turn.

And yet.

That mouth panting into her ear. That hand pawing her breast. Not Larry's. That weight, those thrusts, that cock inside her. Not Larry's. Not anyone's. And yet they were too real, too palpable, to be imaginary. Even as Larry humped away at Maria, someone – no-one – was fucking Anna, too.

"What the–" She fumbled for the lamp.

At the bloom of light, Larry's *"No!"* ricocheted off the walls. Too late. Anna saw what he'd wanted the dark to hide: the grotesque scarring down one side of his torso, from armpit to thigh; the cratered hip, the hollowed buttock. Too late, he pulled out of Maria and rolled away, drawing the sheet over the ancient wounds of his separation.

One brother. Dead.

"He's one of *us*," Maria breathed, as Larry lay there, convulsed with sobs that shook the bed almost as much as the sex had done.

"Was," Anna replied. "He was."

Martyn Bedford

Martyn Bedford is the award-winning author of eight novels and a short-story collection. He is a Senior Lecturer in Creative Writing at Leeds Trinity University.

Frenemies

They are not your friends.

These wolves in Grandmama's bed-clothes, with frilly night-caps pulled low over sharp yellow eyes. *My, what big teeth you have.* They greet you briefly, filling their quota to keep you hanging in their nets, dangling from their hooks. But their warmth is just a ruse. They cannot stand you; they barely endure being kind to you. These wolves circle your battered self, nipping and striking, always drawing blood to keep you down and drained, howling in triumph every time you falter. They only pat you on the back to make sure their daggers are still there, poisoned blades feeding you darkness. Smiles of sympathy are thin veils for blood-thirsty teeth. Hidden with grimaces, they grin at your pain, spit out hollow clichés. They mouth echoes of your woes, and you think they understand you, know you for who you are. You trust them, believing them eager to offer a kind word and a ready hug.

They are not your friends.

They offer you a pedestal, glitter you in lights and faint praise, and pretend to celebrate with you. So dazzled, you cannot see the Damoclean swords dangling in the rafters, sharp points hungry for blood. You do not see the trap door beneath your feet, fragile and ready to break, dumping you into darkness. They orchestrate and pull the strings and you dance, even if you don't like their tune. They set you up so your fall is worse. They feast on your weakness, as they grow stronger with every bite. They are not your friends.

Their words are doubled – *we talked about you* – and though your greedy heart begs to see only good in their words, paranoia sees their wolven teeth gnawing at your soul. They prefer you filled with doubt and self-loathing, and shut you down when you reach out. They do not want you to see beyond their darkness, to discover the truth. You look at just the wrong time/right time and see their true wolven faces, see the reality behind their smoke-and-mirror-friendships. They snarl as their hold on you slips and you are free. Now you have seen past their teeth and darkness, you know they have always been weaker than you. Even as you explore this unusual sensation of freedom, your heart freezes in the sudden cold truth: they were never your friends.

LMA Bauman-Milner

LMA Bauman-Milner is a librarian by light and an author by night. Her first collection of short stories, Dark Doors, *was long-listed for a Saboteur Award in 2016.*

Moobs

You get up in a morning – hazy eyes, bed head, and visible apathy for another day. You have a piss, wrestling to control which way the gushing stream goes. Still half asleep, you reach for the toothbrush and toothpaste. It's second nature now but, as you begin to brush, topless and swaying, you see the jiggle.

You see us staring you down. We taunt you through our fleshy, hairy guise. We whisper threats: "we're only going to get bigger, you fat shit ... people are going to notice us now ... can't wear baggy clothes to hide us forever."

You desperately ache for a time when you didn't have these colossal airbags. You tear at us, frustrated, angry – disappointed in yourself.

"It was no surprise you got fat, you did nothing to prevent it." We are right, but you can't help but feel hard done by. You hold us, you turn left, and you turn right. "No matter which angle, you're still fat." You can't ignore our whispers.

You throw the toothbrush down, desperate and panicked. You have to get out. You turn from the bathroom, you feel worthless, you stumble into the bedroom, you see her ...

I realise. I. Not them. I see her lying there, cats softly asleep - partner on the bed. I may have moobs but somebody loves me. Somebody loves you: moobs or chiselled deity, flab or flat belly, don't let your stupid body define you.

Ethan Lowe

Ethan Lowe has been adopted by the Yorkshire people, despite being from the better side of the Pennines. Theoretical motivator, puckish rogue – forever wondering at what point he can say "I'm a writer."

A Strange Breed

My interest in genetics began when I heard about the liger and the tigon. These are hybrid animals. When a male lion breeds with a female tiger, the resulting offspring is called a liger. The tigon is the reverse, the product of the union of a male tiger and a female lion. Both are rare – not least because lions and tigers do not naturally share a habitat – but have been bred in captivity.

I went on to learn of other examples of hybrids. Perhaps the best known is the mule, a cross between a donkey and a horse. More exotic are the cama, a cross between a camel and a llama; the wholphin – killer whale and dolphin; and the zedonk, the offspring of a zebra and a donkey.

Donkeys themselves are not hybrids. I found this confusing and disappointing, having initially believed them to be a cross between a dog and a monkey. It was this disappointment that determined my future career path. I resolved that I would create a brand new hybrid animal, and knew exactly where to begin.

It only took a few weeks to locate a suitable male monkey offered for sale online, and from there it was a simple matter to find a fertile and appropriately-sized dog as its partner. Initially the pair seemed reluctant to mate, but within days were enthusiastic participants in the project. If anything, this stage of the exercise was too successful. I spent many restless nights regretting my decision to keep the animals in my own home for monitoring purposes.

Their sustained copulation did not, however, result in impregnation, and when, ten months in, the monkey died – probably from exhaustion – I decided to abandon the experiment.

Frustrated by my failure, I gave up on my ambitions for over a year, but my passion was reignited when I attended a party, at which the hosts served vol-au-vent. It occurred to me that the word "vol-au-vent" hints at a hitherto undiscovered hybrid of an elephant and a vole. Thus inspired, I returned to my work with renewed vigour.

The elephant was surprisingly easy to procure, thanks to my contacts in the illegal underground circus industry. Voles are in plentiful supply. This proved fortunate, because while the elephant appeared to suffer no ill effects as a result of my research, the mortality rate among the voles was close to one hundred percent.

Of the survivors, none had been successfully fertilised by the time the elephant escaped from, and indeed destroyed, the shed in which I had housed it. I had made an error in assuming that it would be as engaged in the experiment as the dog and monkey had been. Again I was forced to admit defeat.

After some reflection on my unsuccessful efforts to become a biological pioneer, it struck me that I should turn to the ancients for inspiration. My next project, I decided, would be an attempt to recreate the centaur of Greek myth, a creature said to be half horse and half human. An obvious advantage to this decision was that I myself could be one of the subjects, ensuring that I had at least one reliable participant.

Your honour, I have pleaded guilty to the offences of which I am charged. In deciding the sentence, I hope you will consider the needs of my infant son, who was born with severe health problems, and whose mother is unable and unwilling to care for him. And please be assured that I took no gratification in my work other than that which is inherent in the pursuit of knowledge. I did it all for science.

Joe Williams

Joe Williams is a writer and performing poet from Leeds. He appears regularly at events in Yorkshire and beyond, telling silly stories about things that probably didn't happen, with the occasional moment of heartbreak just to keep you on your toes.

Deathsturbation

I don't think I was in no right frame of mind at the time but I guess that's easy for me to say now it's already happened. It came about when I was desperate. Hannah left me because I was too possessive, too clingy, too much. I was in a bad place. You don't see the waterfall until you're off the edge. You just think you're making steady progress along the river, you feel good, your adrenaline's going.

Then freefall.

I was drunk most of the time, or high, or both. It always went like that after a breakup but Hannah was the one. She tore open my existence while I was with her, and tore it up again when she left. The stitches kept bursting and the wound was infected for a long time. It left an ugly scar, can you see it?

I fell in with people I had no business falling in with. The quiet and reserved boy who got straight As and loved his mother: he was here, in a dive bar with strange men and women who looked beyond hardened by life. It was a bad part of town and that added to it.

One guy pulled me aside. Reeked of old man aftershave and wore a shirt with the buttons half-done and a thick gold chain on his hairy chest. 'You ever been with a guy?' he asked. His voice wet with booze. 'I know a guy likes guys that ain't ever been with guys.'

I told him no.

'Well I know a guy'd pay for you to help him out.'

'Help him how?' I hated the sound of it. I thought of prison showers and public toilets and any other day I would bail, but I was drunk and I was high and I listened.

'He wants you to do him a *favour*, see?'

'Yeah?'

'He wants you to kill him just as he comes.'

'Comes where?' I asked. I knew what he meant, but I'd developed this thing for feigning naivety.

'Oh, you're so innocent. You're perfect.' People at the bar were looking at us. There was a woman taller than life itself and looked just as much of a bitch. 'C'mon. We better leave. He'll pay you big.'

The idea of money lit up my drunken eyes like Vegas. I've never been to Vegas. I followed the man through a haze of vape smoke and out into the cold night. Thought of regretting my decision, but thoughts are intangible little creatures and can be squashed under the right kind of weight.

Then I'm in a car and my head lolls but I still feel that buzz and the passing traffic fades and I see the contemplative face of god as he wonders what on earth went wrong with his people.

I find myself in a bedsit and there's a skinny guy who I guess is around my age but he looks ill. The man from the bar has gone.

'You look just about right.'

'I don't feel it.'

'We never do. That's the sad beauty of life. We see it in others, but never ourselves.' He shuffled on the bare mattress. 'C'mon in. You don't have to touch. Just pick up that sword.'

'What?'

'The katana.'

It glimmered at the foot of the bed and I was unsteady on my feet. It felt light in my hands.

'When I scream 'Hallelujah,' drive it into me.'

It wasn't real. None of it was. Just a hallucination of a broken young man. I grinned as he began to pleasure himself, maintaining eye contact. My eyes drifted. Almost slept.

'Hallelujah!'

The room filled with incandescent light and I drove it down into the base of his throat and his eyes rolled back and blood fountained, painting the white light with cascades of red.

I never got no money and it's cold in this here prison cell.

T.G. Pickup

T.G. Pickup is a writer of novels and short stories and ardent coffee and tattoo fanatic. Find him on Twitter @tgpickup

William Killiam

Adam's chanting, *William, William.*
I hear rustling as he opens my bag and his chanting sounds like a nursery rhyme as it becomes louder:
William, William,
William, Oh, killiam.

Air, warm and stale, rushes over me. Adam's hand wriggles in, closes round me and drags me out. He squeezes a head for me and pats it into shape. He shapes my arms and legs. His fingers sculpt my knees and elbows, fingers and toes.

Adam's breathing is thick and slow as he cleaves and scrapes the front of my new head with something small and sharp. Pinch. Pick. Poke. He gives me eye sockets, a nose, a mouth.

"Now you've got a face," he says. "And I've got some of William's hair for you." His voice is soft, as if I were very special to him. He prods the hair into my head. It hurts but I get used to it and the hair feels long and silky as it flops over my face.

Adam strokes my face. "I've got you some eyes, proper glass ones; they're blue, just like William's." As he pushes the cold glass eyes into their sockets, I wonder what Adam looks like and I feel excited – I'll see him soon! He spits on his finger, wipes the clay off my eyes and his world becomes mine. I'm on his desk, in a dirty pool of light from an angle-poise lamp. Next to my creased, clay-smeared bag, sit a stack of school books, and the metal tool he used to sculpt my face.

William, William, William, Oh killiam, sings Adam. He picks me up and some football boots on a wrinkled bed swing into view. He places me in the palm of his hand and his face appears, scrutinising me. I see his grey eyes are flecked with amber; I note the blackheads peppering his long nose, the faint smudge of an adolescent moustache and the specks of dandruff in his dark hair.

Then I notice his pupils have gone to a pinprick and he's

sneering like a grotesque puppet.

"Hello, William," he says.

Fear pulses inside me as he places me on the desk. Something gleams between his fingers: a piece of glass, sharp and jagged, like the tooth of a primitive beast. He raises it high above me where it glitters for a moment before he plunges it hard into my chest. Pain sears and sings, screams and swings back and forth through my body like a trapeze.

William, William, sings Adam. He holds my head and picks up three long needles. Jab. Jab. Jab.

William, Oh killiam.

He scoops me up and drops me into his blazer pocket. The wrinkled bed, the angle-poise lamp and Adam, are sucked away and everything goes black. I lie, pierced with glass and needles, throbbing with agony and confusion, amongst the fluff, chewing gum wrappers and coins, while Adam sleeps.

The next morning, I hear voices in the school yard.

"… heard about William?"

"… said his head was exploding."

"… in a coma … might even die!"

"… Sorry to hear about yer mate, Adam."

All morning, I try and try until I can move my arms. I grasp the needles and the glass, yank at them until they come out, then smooth the ragged wounds in my chest and head. The relief is sweet as the pain ebbs away.

"Great news!" says Miss Crawshaw in double maths. "William's awake. It's a miracle."

I put my hands to my face and pull my nose until it is long like Adam's. I use one of the needles to speckle my nose with blackheads. I concentrate, focus hard. "Come *on,*" I tell myself. "Be *him.*" I brace myself and stick a needle into my head. I can stand it for a minute or two, so I drive the other two in. With fear and pain coursing through my body, I stab myself with the glass shard.

"I'm Adam," I tell myself. "*Adam,* not William."

Now Miss Crawshaw is asking Adam if he's alright. A moment later he hits the floor.

There's panic in her voice. "Ambulance! ... turn him over ... recovery position."

I tumble out of his pocket and a circle of faces crowds over me.   "... ugh, what's that ..."

"... well creepy ..."

"... pull those needles out of its head ... and the glass ..."
       Yes, get them out. *Please*

"... don't be stupid, it can't feel ..."

"Ellie, get rid of that, that ... *thing*," Miss Crawshaw says.

Fingers, warm and small with pink-varnished nails, pick me up in a careful pincer grip. The crowd stands back, and as Ellie carries me across the classroom, my view of Adam lying on his side, eyes closed, jigs up and down, up and down, then disappears when she drops me in the bin.

Stephanie Buick

If it shimmies like a flamingo dressed as Elvis, then gobbles you up, it's probably in one of Stephanie Buick's stories.

Spork

So, I was at one of these networking events, y'know, where dry-cleaned slimy twonks flick out business cards like smarmy ninjas. The ones that equate speaking to breathing, and when they're 'listening' they boom "Uh Huh" every two seconds.

In the first minute I realised how desperate I'd been since my life splintered and broke in two last year. I'm always at these shitty things and not knowing why.

But this weird thing happened.

I was staring into my coffee cup after failing to strike up conversation again. I've never held an opinion about the weather. The Financial Times makes a better hat than reading matter. And I've never had a favourite dual-carriageway or motorway exit.

Oh, and it makes me queasy to talk about my 'business'.

I was contemplating hiding in the toilets again when I noticed her. A blue streak in her hair. Striking eye liner and, this is going to sound harsh, clumsily drawn lipstick.

She was doing something extraordinary. She was staring at a spoon. No, it was a … what's it called? A spork. She was at the buffet table and staring intently at this fucking spork.

I looked around. No one else had noticed. They were busy shamelessly pitching their businesses. So they were missing this great event, like a performance. Was it a 'thing' to purposely attract more business? If so, it'll be considered one of the greatest pitches ever. I mean, was she a product analyst? An inspector from the Spork Quality Council? A corporate-loving conceptual artist?

I had to approach. I didn't even think about it. I had to say something that wasn't work related.

So I said, "Oh, hey, is that a spork?" I know it was dumb.

"Yes," she said. And carried on looking at it. And kept looking at it. I was looking at her and she was looking at the spork. Maybe if someone was looking at me this could have gone viral. But I had no patience to force that. I had to find out what she was doing.

"Is ... is something happening?" I asked.

She stopped looking at the spork, and her eyes turned to me. I thought I was about to be shot down.

"I've been working on a thesis," she said. "This 'spork' is made up from two completely different tools. Tools that work well individually and have no issues by themselves. But they've been formed together in an attempt at efficiency. But it's not more efficient. So why has it been done? Let me ask: Why do you use a spork?"

"Erm ... if I'm on a plane, I guess. Or if I have a picnic."

"Exactly. It's for travel. So what does that imply? It implies that these two things have been formed together because they make better traveling partners. But they're not as effective as they are when they're used separately. They're a compromise. But one that has been accepted. Agreed upon, like two people agreeing upon a life together as a compromise. The spork is two tools traveling together as one unit, like a relationship. The spork is love. Well, that's the thesis, anyway."

I had not listened properly. Or maybe I had. I was still waiting for her pitch.

But she just put it down and left.

I considered running after her but no one should have to see an adult run in brogues. I could've said something witty and asked if she wanted to go to a restaurant to stare at cutlery. I wanted her to lecture me about sporks.

I then realised that I was holding her business card. Look, I have it here. I must have taken it from her at some point. Her company is called 'Salad Queen'. It says she does: 'Business Development'.

So that's what I was going ask: do you think I should ring her?

Lewis King

Lewis King (@squirrellking) MA Creative Writing graduate and compere of WordSpace Open Mic. Follow on Twitter and Instagram.

It's Over

Sitting on the bed, I trace my fingers over the stitching of the suitcase. I lift a shirt, half-heartedly fold it, and place it inside. What should I bother packing? What do I even need?

She's left, for the evening anyway, for me to collect my things. 'Essentials,' she said. She'll box the rest later. How do I know what my essentials are? She was essential to me. There's a picture in the corner of us smiling, happy … and content? I had it framed as a Christmas present. Was she pleased with it? I sift through my memories looking for signs. I pick up the picture, wrap it in a T-shirt and place it in my case. If she doesn't want me, she doesn't need the picture.

If she was here and I was packing for a trip, she'd be tutting at me already, impatient, but then she'd help, joking at my 'uselessness,' and we'd end up in a pile on the bed, laughing. Though the last time that happened was ages ago: less giggling, more niggling these days, I guess.

At the dresser, I scoop out the contents and dump them in the case. Pants: I don't need to think about those, they can all go in. In the wardrobe, I notice, as if for the first time, that I generally rotate the same four outfits. When did I start doing that? I pull the hangers across, screeching on the railing as they go. There's a shirt I haven't seen in a long time – purple and blue with black palm trees – that I used to love: cheesy and fun. She hated it. I even rescued it once from a bag she'd made up for the charity shop.

Suddenly decisive, I pack the shirt. I find some shorts, flip-flops. I grab my credit card and passport. I almost forgot! The box under the bed with my swimming gear and underwater camera. A few more 'essentials' and I realise there's not enough space now. I carefully remove the photo frame and place it on the bed, before snapping the case shut.

Lucy Medes-Hinken

Lucy Medes-Hinken, Leeds Trinity alumna, hates writing bios.

Frenemy

Reverend Haliday took up his post one year ago to the day. He left the comfortable surroundings of his youth and education, and travelled far into the north country. When he stepped out of the carriage on that first day he sensed that the lonely chapel had been waiting for him his entire life. He had never seen such a place before; an endless sky, green rolling valleys as far as the eye could see. It felt untouched. Here there would time for contemplation, and the prayer he felt he so needed. He would find himself here, become still, and whole once more.

The year that followed, however, had made quite different plans for him. The Reverend could scarcely make time for himself what with one thing or another, and yet at the end of each day a most debilitating loneliness set in. Though he kept up his correspondences, he found that whenever he received a letter from his old friend Maloy, his mood would descend further. When Maloy announced he intended to visit, Haliday avoided answering him. The prospect of such a visit in fact weighed heavily on him.

It was a fine morning in early May when Maloy appeared unexpectedly. Haliday had been out in the fields when a farm boy approached him carrying word of a man waiting for him in the chapel. His pitchfork fell to the ground with a thud as he collapsed on a shady embankment nearby, suddenly bewildered by the news. He wondered whether it was exhaustion overcoming him, for he had stayed with Eliza Entwistle throughout the night until she had breathed her last. She had been a good woman, he knew, not gifted with beauty or opportunity, but always generous in spirit, with a ready smile. That morning, as he piled hay into the carts, he had felt her face behind him, pressing near. But now as he thought of Maloy, he felt her moving away. Haliday looked to the chapel below. He summoned his strength, and climbed to his feet. "This must be swift," he muttered, marching down the hill.

He found the door ajar, and lingered outside for a moment,

looking back at the forgotten graves and the overgrown path. He felt different here now, as if he'd never been here before. *What nonsense*, he thought. He braced himself, and then let his footsteps pierce the silence inside the chapel.

Maloy rose slowly from a seat he'd taken near the entrance and the two men embraced in the aisle. They then sat, staring forward in the dull light of the empty room. In the moments that followed, Maloy recounted his news: of the position he'd been given in his father's investment firm, of Anne, the pretty wife he'd found, of the child that was due by the end of the year. Haliday listened intently with an unwavering smile, but grew aware that Maloy was avoiding making eye contact with him as he spoke. Haliday looked searchingly at his old friend. It was true, Maloy had grown into a handsome dignified young gentleman, but Haliday knew as plain as day that he had never worked for his good fortune, and that he had grown far too self-satisfied with his lot.

"Now tell me, Haliday, just what has happened to you up here in this God-forsaken place?" Maloy then asked.

"There's the point," Haliday replied, though feeling he had already lost his grip on the exchange. Indeed, he felt stricken at having to frame himself in such vulgar terms. He wanted to laugh off the simplicity of his question, but Maloy's eyes were fixed on him. They seemed vicious, unflinching. Haliday knew he was being measured. He became acutely conscious of himself and of his deeds, as if they, as if he, were somehow farcical. He could feel himself losing the calm composure that he so wanted to present to Maloy. He had known this would happen. *This must be swift*, he remembered, loosening his tongue.

Sean Dorrington

Sean Dorrington is an aspiring novelist from Huddersfield, West Yorkshire. His interests include classic literature, politics, philosophy and music.

Nicknames

Lacey can be a bit insufferable sometimes. She's apparently an introvert, but is simultaneously one of the most hyperactive and chatty people I know. I suppose that's because when we hang out we're not usually around other people. As intense as she can be, I'm glad she's being herself.

Each time we meet, Lacey seems to develop a unique nickname for me.

"Yo Sam-Jam! Jammy. SJ. Check this out!"

"Hey, Brosam!"

"How's it going, Sam-a-Lamb?"

"Dude, check it. I thought up a great wrestler nickname for you. SLAM. Or, you know, Slammy, for cutes."

It's a miracle she hasn't run out yet. I've tried to do it myself, but wordplay isn't my strong point, and 'Lacey-Casey-Stacey' is about as far as I can get before running out of mashups entirely. Sometimes she recycles a few, but I can excuse that. Lacey never misses an opportunity to dish out a nickname or two.

That's how I knew something wasn't right.

"Hey, Sam," she murmured, dangling her legs over the edge of the bed and avoiding my gaze. As far as I could tell, she hadn't been doing anything at all. Normally the TV's blazing out the bright colours of her favourite retro platformer, or the bed is strewn about with paper and pencils, but this time she was just sitting there, huddled with a blanket over her head.

"What's the matter?"

"Nothin. Just cold," she lied. I sifted through the game cartridges and art supplies scattered about the carpet so I could sit next to her.

"Doesn't seem like nothing," I prompted, tentatively shifting my weight so that I could lean on my elbows. She didn't stir, and there was a long pause before either of us spoke again. Thankfully, it was Lacey who did.

"Don't you think it's about time I grew up?"

"What?"

"I mean, I'm twenty years old. You're learning how to drive. Natalie Burkes, my dorm-mate from last year? She's getting married. And practically *everyone* in my class has a paying job," she sighed, pulling the blanket further over her head. "I'm doing none of that."

I launched myself upright again at this remark. That kind of thinking seemed a little too deep to brush off. Not missing a beat, I tried my best to set her straight.

"Yeah, but even you said you're gonna do some of those things when you're ready, and you don't have to do them all at once."

"But, like, what about everything else? Everyone says I shouldn't be collecting figurines or watching cartoons. Everyone says I'm a manchild, and I'm a woman. A womild. Everyone says people who 'don't act their age' need to grow up, and I'm starting to believe it's true."

"Hold the phone, who's 'everyone'?" I knew I'd never said anything of the sort, but groups of four or more people were considered the world's population in Lacey's eyes.

"Y'know, everyone. Art club folks. Other people have said it, too. It's just one of those things. But maybe I don't wanna 'go out and have a drink with the bros.' Maybe I wanna stay in and watch Nebula Heroes, play Princess Panic, or read The Last Snowflake. Hell yeah, it's not cool, I'm not cool, but why should I pretend I enjoy doing what I don't? Is that what 'growing up' is about?" She gestured to no-one, almost falling off the bed as she threw her arms forward.

"No? And exactly? You don't have to pretend to be someone you're not, Lace. That's what makes you a responsible adult – you get to make your own decisions. And that's fine. I mean, so long as what you enjoy doing isn't murder or whatever."

That made her laugh. Seems like I'd finally gotten through to her. My friend emerged from her woolly cocoon and grinned widely.

"Thanks for cheering me up, Bal-Sam-ic Vinegar."

"Ugh, that one? At least I know for sure you're back to your old self …"

"Wanna order a pizza and play Drill Racer until we hate each other?"

"You know I do."

Jasmin Lydia Williams

Jasmin Williams has written a large collection of unfinished stories, hoping she'll live to see the day she completes one, if she could only stop having new ideas every five minutes.

Bliar

I saw him from the foot-bridge, flitting like a shadow between the trees. He was heading for the river and I knew instinctively he was up to no good. It had been pouring with rain for over a week which left the fast-flowing Wharfe frothing at the mouth, roaring like some crazed beast on the prowl. No one in their right mind would go anywhere near it in this weather, yet here he was.

"Hey!" I shouted. "You there!"

He glanced up, Judas-faced, and I noticed he was carrying a bulging canvas sack. He glared at me, then carried on scrambling.

I know what you're up to, you brute, I thought. *I won't let you do it. I can't.* I ran to the end of the bridge and made my way towards him. Mud sucked at my shoes, making me slide all over the place. If I wasn't careful, I'd end up in the river myself.

As I got closer, I watched, horrified, as he took something out of the bag and tossed it into the most tumultuous section of water. It disappeared in one gulp. A puppy? A kitten? I strained for a better look as he reached back into the sack. It was then I saw that the thing wriggling to be set free wasn't an animal. It was ... a word. *Brexit.*

"What on earth?"

He flinched but didn't turn round. He was wrestling with the word, forcing it under the water. Bubbles rose to the surface as it gasped for air. He gave one final push and it let go, vanishing into the depths.

"If you're not going to help me, get lost," he said. "I mean it. I'll be drowning your kind any minute now."

"My kind?"

"New Liberals. They're in here somewhere."

"I'm not a New Liberal," I said, offended.

"Conservatives, then."

"I'm not one of those either," I snapped. My stomach tightened. "Look, you can't judge me, you don't know me, but that's beside the point. I think you need help. You can't drown words."

He turned and glared at me. "Why not?"

I shuffled my feet. "It's kind of … pointless."

A large vein in his neck throbbed. "These words are bloody dangerous," he said. "Haven't you seen the devastation they've caused? They have to go."

I thought for a moment. "I don't like them either but … surely it's not the words themselves that cause the problems? It's the people using them."

He hesitated. Two rogue phrases leapt out of the bag making their bid for freedom. *Twitter* and *Facebook*. He tightened his grip on the mouth of the sack as I scrambled after them.

"Let them go," he said. "There's far worse than that in here."

I glanced around. Maybe he was right, maybe the words did have to go. Something had to change. I'd been telling myself for years I needed to do more, say more, take action; and here I was, being offered a chance, and I was dithering.

I stepped towards him and lowered my voice. "Are you … a *Corbynista*?" No answer. "Let me see what else you've got," I said.

He opened the bag a smidgen. *Daily Mail*, *Weaponise* and *Austerity* yelped and squealed, their puppy-dog I's pleading. Beneath them, a shadowy figure spat and hissed to get free. The man reached in trying to catch it.

"This word will never go down without a fight," he said. "But it is the worst of the lot, we have to destroy it."

"Ok," I said, warily.

"I'm warning you. It has a strange power over people and will say anything, *anything* to regain control. But you have to ignore it – you have to catch every slick phrase that comes spinning out of it and destroy it, because I promise you, it's lethal."

"Ready?" he said.

I nodded. At last, he hauled the word out. I gasped. *Blairite*. The deadliest formation I'd ever seen. It snarled and bit at his hand as he fought to restrain it. Holding the word by the neck, the man squeezed tight and, just like he said, clever little expressions spewed all over the place. One phrase coiled round my ankle, hoping to drag me under. *I'm just like everyone else in this country*, it said, sporting a malicious grin.

"That's it," I said, grabbing it by the throat. "I'm in."

Andrea Hardaker

Andrea Hardaker is a blethering skite; one who talks a lot. She loves writing because blank pages let her talk all over them.

Spirenti

"Ye think ah cannae see ye? Well, yer wrong. Ah can see ye right enough. Devouring me, laying me bare.

And then, yer off. Playing the room, ay watching me. Ye sidle forth and no *wan* o' them sees yer true goal. They're oblivious to yer sleekit glances. The way yer heart beats its amorous tune as ye' edge past them aw. Each greeting, each inanity, each *pointless* interaction, a masquerade.

There's nae escape fae me. Ah recognise the temptress within, the seductress, the siren, hell, even the whore ... shining like a beacon, luring ye into mah snare. Is it mah fault? Och, no, a dinnae think sae. The malaise is yours, no mine.

Yer nearly here noo. Ah've nae choice. Yer greedy eyes consume me. Yer feverish mouth quivers at the mere thought o' mah taste on yer hot lips. And, yer hands shake, as they reach oot, coorse and clumsy in their haste to own me ... to uncork me ... to breathe in mah heady scent.

Ye pull me to yer chest, wrap me tight beneath yer jerkin and away we sneak to the seafront, so you can have me like a demon possessed. Ye glug your fill. Plunder me. Drain me, and then discard me to the sea. Nae message of love. Nae farewell!

Just, an empty bottle cast aside."

Liz Mistry

Liz Mistry writes crime fiction and so far has had two novels published. She studied Creative Writing at Leeds Trinity University graduating with an MA in 2016.

all I ask of you

is a long term commitment

to tolerate me

With special thanks for additional haiku contributions from:

Kathryn Wharton - p.10
Tim Leadbeater   - p.11
Clare Wigzell   - p.12
Liz Mistry   - p.34
Lewis King   - p.35
Martyn Bedford   - p.36
Joe Williams   - p.62

Indigo Dreams Publishing Ltd
24, Forest Houses
Cookworthy Moor
Halwill
Beaworthy
Devon
EX21 5UU
www.indigodreams.co.uk